The Gorgeous Georgians & the Vile Victorians Quiz Book

Terry Deary & Martin Brown

Scholastic Children's Books,
Commonwealth House, 1-19 New Oxford Street,
London WC1A 1NU, UK

A division of Scholastic Ltd
London ~ New York ~ Toronto ~ Sydney ~ Auckland
Mexico City ~ New Delhi ~ Hong Kong

Published in this edition by Scholastic Ltd, 2003

Material in this book has previously been published in
Horrible Histories: The Horribly Huge Quiz Book
and other Horrible Histories titles.

Text copyright © Terry Deary, 1999–2002
Illustrations copyright © Martin Brown, 1994–99

ISBN 0 439 97731 2

Printed in Dubai, U.A.E.

2 4 6 8 10 9 7 5 3 1

The right of Terry Deary and Martin Brown to be identified as the author
and illustrator of this work respectively has been asserted by them in accordance
with the Copyright, Designs and Patents Act, 1988.

Contents

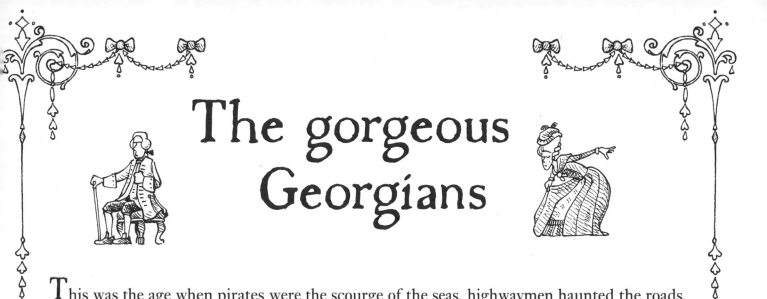

The gorgeous Georgians

This was the age when pirates were the scourge of the seas, highwaymen haunted the roads, a crackpot was king and the French and Americans were revolting . . . some things never change. It was also the age of thick make-up, beauty spots, monstrous wigs and padded bosoms – and that was just the men.

Quick questions

1. German George I took the throne in 1714. But where was his wife Dorothea? (Clue: she flirted once too often)

2. In Banff in 1714 the town hangman had to catch stray dogs. He was paid for each dog he caught. How did he prove he'd caught a dog? (Clue: hide!)

3. In 1717 a Scottish teacher murdered two pupils in his charge. Before he was hanged he had an odd punishment. What was it? (Clue: he'd never write on a blackboard again)

4. In 1718 the dreaded pirate Blackbeard was shot and beheaded by a navy officer. Blackbeard's body was thrown over the side of the ship. What's supposed to have happened next? (Clue: maybe he crawled)

5. Many Georgian pirates wore gold ear-rings. Why? (Clue: go to see?)

6. In 1722 an elephant died on its way to Dundee. What did Doctor Patrick Blair do with the corpse? (Clue: jumbo scientist)

7. In 1724 murderer Maggie Dickson escaped execution. The law said she couldn't be hanged. Why? (Clue: second time lucky)

8. In 1727 George I's hated wife, Dorothea, died. He set off for the funeral but failed to get there. Why? (Clue: a second funeral delayed him)

9. Soon after George I died a raven flew in at the window of his girlfriend, the Duchess of Kendal. She looked after it better than any pet. Why? (Clue: it was something George had crowed about)

10. In 1739 the famous highwayman, Dick Turpin, was executed. His handwriting was recognized by someone who knew him at school and he was betrayed. Who betrayed Turpin? (Clue: master of treachery)

11. How can a hot poker cure toothache? (Clue: ear we go again)

12. George II and his family ate Sunday dinner in style. What could the public buy on those Sundays? (Clue: feeding time at the zoo?)

13. In the sport of 'Goose Riding' a live goose was hung from a tree branch by its feet. The competitor climbed on a horse. What did he have to do to win? (Clue: the best rider would win by a neck)

14. In 1743 George II became the last British monarch to lead an army into battle at Dettingen, Germany. But his horse disgraced him. How? (Clue: might have made a good race horse)

15. In 1746 James Reid played his bagpipes in York. He never played them again. Why not? (Clue: the noise he made was criminal)

16. In 1747 Lord Lovat became the last person to be beheaded in the Tower of London. As he went to his death 20 other innocent people died. How? (Clue: curiosity killed the cat)

17. In 1748 George II's oldest son, Prince Frederick, was hit with a tennis ball in the stomach. How did it affect him in 1751? (Clue: we've never had a King Fred)

18. A gang of smugglers caught a law officer and left him for dead after teaching him not to be too nosey. What did they do? (Clue: how did he smell?)

19. In 1755 an old man was buried at a crossroads in Cornwall with a stake through his heart. What had he done? (Clue: he brought it on himself)

20. Georgians ate cooked tomatoes but never raw tomatoes. Why not? (Clue: doctor's orders)

21. At a 1758 fair one of the attractions was a man eating a chicken. What was so unusual about this? (Clue: it took guts)

22. In 1758 Georgians started using bank notes as well as coins. This was followed by a new crime. What? (Clue: copy-cats)

23. When George III came to the throne in 1760 the cruel crowds cried 'Pug!' at the queen. Why? (Clue: not puppy love)

24. What would a Georgian lady do with a dead mouse? (Clue: modern women use a pencil instead)

25. In 1762 a sheep thief tied the back legs of a sheep together and threw the rope around his neck to help him carry it. He hanged for his theft . . . but in a weird way. How? (Clue: the sheep's revenge?)

26. In 1770 Captain James Cook claimed a new country for England. The natives objected and threatened him with a weapon the Brits had never seen before. What? (Clue: the answer will come back to you)

27. In 1773 Americans rebelled against British taxes on things like tea. What did they do with tea chests arriving in British ships? (Clue: a new way to make tea?)

28. In 1776 a lady wore a hat at a picnic, which had decorative fruit and vegetables pinned to it. A cow ate the hat. What happened next? (Clue: how do you turn a cow to beef?)

29. In 1788 an Edinburgh councillor, Deacon Brodie, invented a hanging machine with a trapdoor. How did the Deacon prove that it worked? (Clue: first hand experience)

30. Posh Georgian ladies wore tight iron belts to give them amazingly thin waists. Elizabeth Evelyn's belt killed her, which was especially sad. Why? (Clue: too small to begin with)

31. In 1790 a sailor disguised himself as a woman to avoid being forced to join the navy. The navy spotted his disguise and took him anyway. How did they spot him? (Clue: it should have been a close shave)

32. 'Women fainted at the sight, children screamed and dogs yelped,' in the 1790s. What did men start wearing that caused this sensation? (Clue: get ahead, get a hat)

33. King George III suffered periods of mental illness. During one attack he dressed in black in memory of, 'That good man,' whom he believed to be dead. Who? (Clue: if George had been well he'd have known the man was alive)

34. In 1797 the rebellious pupils at Rugby public school decided to break into the headmaster's room. What did they use to get through the thick door? (Clue: it wasn't even the fifth of November)

35. Why did Georgian dentists buy tusks of hippo and walrus? (Clue: fangs very much)

36. How old were the youngest chimney sweeps in 1804? (Clue: not infants)

37. How was Lord Nelson's body brought home after his death at Trafalgar in 1805? (Clue: not a barrel of laughs)

38. John Bellingham blamed the government for ruining his business. How did he get his revenge in 1812? (Clue: a blow to the head)

39. Napoleon lost the Battle of Waterloo in 1815. What did Brit General Lord Raglan lose? (Clue: 'armless sort of chap)

40. In 1817 Brixton prison invented a new punishment for criminals. What? (Clue: hamster toy)

41. In 1818 Mary Shelley wrote a horrific story that is still popular today. What is it called? (Clue: frankly monstrous)

42. In 1820 in Scotland a rebel weaver was the last man to be sentenced to an ancient punishment. What? (Clue: long and drawn out)

43. In 1821 Queen Caroline died. What did this odd queen put on her head to keep cool while she was out riding? (Clue: American pie)

44. In 1822 King George IV visited Scotland and wore a kilt. How did he keep his knees warm? (Clue: they weren't loose)

45. In 1823 a boy at a public school, William Webb Ellis, cheated at football and invented a new game. What? (Clue: you have to hand it to him)

46. In 1830 the Liverpool to Manchester railway opened. How did Liverpool MP William Huskisson celebrate? (Clue: it's a knockout)

47. In 1831 the north-eastern port of Sunderland brought in a new import. What? (Clue: dis eez a horrible thing to suffer)

Dreadful down under

In 1788 the first convicts arrived at Port Jackson in Australia. Can you answer these questions on terrible transportation?

48. The Aborigine people shouted 'Warra! Warra!' at the convicts. What does it mean?
a) G'day! G'day!
b) Funny people! Funny people!
c) Go away! Go away!

49. There were about 20,000 Aborigines living on Tasmania when the British first arrived in 1802. How many Aborigines were there by 1880?
a) 30,000
b) 5,000
c) 0

50. What were 'bushrangers'?
a) Aborigine hunters
b) British settlers
c) British criminals who were left to wander through the bush instead of going to prison

51. Of the first convicts to arrive, how old was the youngest?
a) nineteen
b) fifteen
c) nine

Foul for females

What was it like for Georgian women? Try this simple test – answer true or false. . .

52. Georgian women put cork balls in their cheeks to improve their appearance.

53. The average age for women to get married was 15.

54. A woman could be burned alive for murdering her husband.

55. Georgian wives were sometimes sold by their husbands at auction.

56. Men were allowed to beat their wives with sticks.

57. Ladies used cement as make-up.

58. The average wage for a maid was £3 a month.

59. Georgian women often took snuff.

60. A group of Welsh women stopped an invasion by the French.

61. It was fashionable for women to have a sun tan.

Out of time

Can you spot which of these things were first seen in 1700s Britain?

Test your teacher

Teachers love asking questions. They even get *paid* for it! Now it's your chance to get your revenge. Test your teacher (or pester your parent) with this amazingly difficult quiz. When they get a wrong answer you can mutter, 'I thought you'd have known that!'

73. What did a Georgian doctor use to pull out rotten teeth?
a) a penguin
b) a pelican
c) a puffin

74. In 1750 a gentleman fed a dish of smuggled tea to what?
a) a dog
b) a cat
c) a rat

75. Where did Robinson Cruso live?
a) King's Lynn, Norfolk
b) on a desert island
c) in a deserted Ireland

76. In 1774 a Huntingdon highwayman held up a coach using what?
a) a walking stick
b) a candlestick
c) a bag of sick

77. Georgian gentlemen in Britain would not wear what?
a) flared trousers
b) pink trousers
c) any trousers

78. What did sailors use their stale cheese supplies for?
a) carved it into buttons
b) fed it to rats and the rats broke their teeth and starved to death
c) grated it and stuffed their mattresses with it

79. Carlisle Spedding invented a 'steel mill' – it struck sparks off a flintstone and gave light. Useful for pitmen in a coal mine. How did Spedding die?
a) he trapped a finger in his steel mill and it turned poisonous
b) his steel mill caused an explosion of gas in a coal mine
c) a dissatisfied miner smashed the steel mill over Spedding's head

80. What did some racist Georgians do to foreigners on the streets of London?
a) threw books entitled 'Learn yourself English' at them
b) threw Scotsmen at them
c) threw dead cats and dogs at them

81. What useful thing did the watch-maker Andrew Cumming invent in 1775 that we still use today?
a) a think-tank
b) a chin-strap
c) a stink-trap

82. The Georgians enjoyed watching hounds tearing hares apart. But when was the sport stopped?
a) when the hare waved a white flag
b) when Queen Victoria was splattered with hare blood in 1899
c) never

IF THEIR DOG GOT TORN UP, WOULD THEY STILL ENJOY IT?

Foreign affairs

Sometimes letters from abroad are opened and read by a government 'censor'. He cuts out unsuitable words or phrases. That's what happened to these letters. Can you guess what's missing?

83. *Japan, 1703.*
...Samurai warriors cut off Kira's ▮▮▮▮ and put it on their dead lord's grave.

84. *Gold Coast, Africa, 1708.*
I am becoming filthy rich because I get well paid for each ▮▮▮▮ I send to America.

85. *Florida, 1739.*
...then the Spanish coastguards took the ▮▮▮▮ of a British sailor, Robert Jenkins. This means war!

86. *Naples, 1748.*
...and when we excavated the ruins we came across a perfectly preserved ▮▮▮▮

87. *Russia, 1762.*
Tsar Peter has been assassinated. He was a very rude man and used to show his ▮▮▮▮ to priests during services.

88. *Paris, 1770.*
...now that French artist Boucher has shocked everyone with a painting of a ▮▮▮▮

89. *Austria, 1776.*
...the Emperor says it is no longer against the law to be a ▮▮▮▮

90. *America, 1777.*
As we were about to cut off one ▮▮▮▮ in the hospital a cannonball crashed through and blew off the other!

91. *Hawaii, 1779.*
Sadly our captain and great explorer, Captain Cook, was murdered in a row over a ▮▮▮▮

92. *Rome, 1780.*
I was amazed to see Mr Galvani use this electricity stuff to bring life to a dead ▮▮▮▮

93. *The Atlantic Ocean, 1782.*
Of course British ships are faster because they have a ▮▮▮▮

94. *France, 1792.*
I watched as the French tested a new execution machine, a guillotine, on a suitable ▮▮▮▮

Words: tongue, naked woman, frog, leg, witch, slave, corpse, copper bottom, skeleton, ear, boat, head

A revolutionary question

95. Where did the French revolutionaries buy their guillotines?

Chop and change

The French Revolution was famous for its automatic neck-chopper, the guillotine. But which of the following foul facts are true? Answer in French, s'il vous plait. 'Oui' for yes or 'Non' for no. Queen Marie Antoinette's wigs for winners – a pain in the neck for losers.
Oui or non...?

96. The man who designed the French version of the guillotine was Doctor Joseph-Ignace Guillotin.

97. The chopping machine wasn't always called a guillotine. At first it was named a Louisette. Criminals later nicknamed it 'The Widow'.

98. The guillotine's designer said that all the victim felt was a chill on the back of the neck.

99. There was a rule that said French women should be taught about the Revolution. They were encouraged to take their knitting to the executions and watch.

100. One woman who cashed in on the executions was Madame Marie Tussaud. She made 'death masks' of the famous heads out of wax and took them fresh from the guillotine basket.

101. The people of Lyon suffered mass guillotine sessions because few people there had supported the Revolution. The guillotine couldn't get through the necks quickly enough in the city of Lyon so the revolutionaries brought in good old firing squads to help kill more.

102. King Louis XVI gave advice to inventor of the guillotine. We'll never know whether the King was impressed by the result when the machine was later used to chop his own head off!

103. The machine's first live victim was a highwayman.

104. Many people turned up to watch the first execution using the guillotine. But they were disappointed and thought hangings were much more fun.

105. The French Revolution started on 14 July 1789, but the guillotine wasn't brought into service for another three years.

106. Head-chopping machines had been in use in Britain 200 years earlier than the French Revolution's guillotine.

Wacky words

Can you match the following Georgian words to their meanings. . .?

107. grunter	a) idiot
108. hock–docky	b) hangman's noose
109. sumph	c) police constable
110. scrag	d) horse
111. bolly dog	e) shoe
112. big bug	f) eye
113. squeezer	g) shilling coin
114. sad man	h) neck
115. daisy-kicker	i) trouble-maker
116. killer	j) important man

The vile Victorians

This was the age of Charles Dickens, of horrible historical slums, of vile Victorian villains, gloomy factories and deep, dark, deadly mines. Not to mention school for everyone, and Jack the Ripper... You might ask, 'Which is worse?'

Quick questions

1. In 1837 Victoria became Queen. How old was she? (Clue: not old enough to vote in those days!)

2. In 1842 women were banned from doing something they had been doing for hundreds of years. What? (Clue: mine, all mine!)

3. Which town was condemned by a government report as being 'the filthiest and unhealthiest of all British towns' in 1842? (Clue: not English, Irish or Welsh)

4. In 1844 a lady wrote that people were pleased when they smelled bad drains. Why? (Clue: red sky at night)

5. 1845 saw the start of a terrible famine in Ireland. Which crop had failed and caused the Hunger, as it was known? (Clue: not chips)

6. Where did the Battle of Widow MacCormack's Cabbage Garden take place, in 1846? (Clue: Celtic)

7. In 1846 a 16-year-old boy was charged with travelling on a train on a 12-year-old's half-price ticket. What was his excuse? (Clue: time to grow)

8. London 'toshers' waded though sewage every day – up to 1.5 metres of the stuff. Why? (Clue: a golden opportunity)

9. In 1847 the Irish were crowding on to 'coffin ships'. Why? (Clue: they've had their chips)

10. In 1848 many European countries were in revolt. The British rebels, the Chartists, had a rally in London but it was a failure. Why? (Clue: it's a wash out)

11. The Great Exhibition took place in 1851.

It was held in a beautiful building designed by Joseph Paxton. What was unusual about it? (Clue: hot house)

12. In 1852 in London a small room is opened for men in Fleet Street and they are very relieved! Why? (Clue: gents still use them)

13. In 1853, Australia got stroppy and refused to take any more from Britain. What? (Clue: if they're barred from Australia they'll be barred in Britain)

14. In 1855 Florence Nightingale was nursing Brit soldiers who were fighting the Russians. What happened to their amputated limbs? (Clue: it will make you pig sick)

15. The first telegraph cable was laid in 1858. Something unfortunate happened to it just four weeks later. What? (Clue: ping!)

16. Punching opponents and gouging their eyes was banned in which sport in 1863? (Clue: players put their foot in it)

17. Irish rebels in 1866 invaded which British territory? (Clue: they mounted a successful defence)

18. Wilkie Collins wrote a novel called *The Moonstone* in 1868. It was the very first of its kind. What kind of novel was it? (Clue: you would need a clue!)

19. In 1869 sailors were banned from wearing something. What? (Clue: it's a close shave)

20. When this man died in 1870 it was said he was 'exhausted by fame'. Who was he? (Clue: no more Christmas Carols)

21. In 1870 a new law forced everyone to do it, even poor little children. What? (Clue: you had to join the class war)

22. In 1871 explorer Henry Stanley found a famous Scot missionary in the heart of Africa. Everyone knows he said, 'Doctor Livingstone, I presume.' But what was the Doctor's one-word reply? (Clue: that's right!)

23. In 1876 Queen Victoria was given an extra title. What was it? (Clue: she wasn't im-pressed)

24. In 1879 the Tay Bridge collapsed and a train with almost 100 passengers sank. The bridge inspector had said it was safe. How many bridges had he inspected before? (Clue: not enough)

25. A Christmas first happened in the United States around 1880. What was it? (Clue: very illuminating)

26. In 1880 the famous writer George Eliot died. What's unusual about him? (Clue: he isn't)

27. SS *Daphne* was launched on the river Clyde and the workers got a huge surprise. What? (Clue: duck!)

28. General Gordon was killed defending Khartoum in the Sudan in 1885. They say he went to battle with a cane in one hand and what in the other? (Clue: God help him!)

29. In 1888 the police named a murderer even though they never caught him (or her). Who? (Clue: and Jill?)

30. In 1890 a man died. He had been cruelly put on show to the ghoulish public because of his unusual illness. It made him look like what? (Clue: big ears)

31. In the 1890 the American army fought the Battle of Wounded Knee. Who were they fighting against? (Clue: a type of Native American)

32. Copy-cat Blackpool built a copy of the Eiffel Tower in 1894. But is the Blackpool Tower bigger or smaller than the French one? (Clue: it's one or the other!)

33. In 1896 Londoners saw 'Boxing Kangaroos' in Australia. How? (Clue: somebody shot the kangaroos)

34. In 1896 motorists were glad to see the back of a rule that slowed them down. What rule? (Clue: they weren't glad to see the back of this man)

35. What did the Victorians join a goose club for? (Clue: they weren't geese-fanciers!)

36. In 1899 Percy Pilcher fell 10 metres and was killed. What did he fall from? (Clue: he was hanging around)

37. Queen Victoria's son-in-law, Prince Christian, lost an eye in a shooting accident. At dinner parties he entertained guests with his collection of what? (Clue: quite a sight)

38. During the Second Boer War in South Africa, what did Victoria order to be sent to each of her 'dear, brave soldiers'? (Clue: very sweet of her)

39. In 1901 old Queen Victoria died and was popped into her coffin. The family lined up to see her. How did they show their respect? (Clue: x)

40. Victorian postmen were nicknamed 'Robins' because of their red uniforms. But why were their uniforms red? (Clue: it was the Royal Mail)

A royal question

41. Queen Victoria came to the throne after William IV. What have William the Fourth and Popeye the Sailor got in common?

Umms and errs

The Victorians were very fond of melodramas. Before the days of television soap operas took place in thrilling theatres where villainous Victorians battled against hapless heroes. You just *know* what they are going to say . . . or do you?

LADIES AND GENTLEMEN! THE VICTORIAN THEATRE PROUDLY PRESENTS SOME TRULY PULSATING, BUT PALPABLY PATHETIC AND PREDICTABLE PEOPLE IMITATED BY INIMICALLY AWFUL ACTORS WHO KEEP FORGETTING THEIR WORDS! CAN YOU HELP? PUT IN THE RIGHT WORD WHERE THEY ERR!

42. East Lynne
Poor Isabel leaves her husband but sneaks back (disguised as a governess) to nurse her sickly son. He dies in her arms as Isabel cries...

Oh, Willie, my child! Dead! Dead! Dead! And never called me errrr!

43. Youth
A bunch of English soldiers struggle against the enemy who must be evil because they aren't English. (The Victorians could be nasty racists.) Their colonel encourages them...

Remember, Great England is looking at you! Show how her sons can fight and errr!

44. The Fatal Marriage
Poor Isabella loses her husband and marries a dear friend. Then her first husband returns. She tries to murder him then decides to stab herself instead. (Don't try this at home.) Isabella sobs...

When I am dead, forgive me and errr me!

45. The Harp of Altenberg
Our heroine, Innogen, is captured by the villain, Brenno. As she tries to escape he grabs hold of her and Innogen cries...

Errrr me!

46. Sweeney Todd or, The Barber of Fleet Street
Sweeney Todd the Barber cuts the throats of customers and drops the corpses into his cellar. There his next-door neighbour collects the bodies and chops them up to make meat pies. As Sweeney cuts a throat he cries...

I errrr them off!

47. Maria Marten or, Murder in the Red Barn
Based on a true 1827 murder. William Corder waits in the barn for sweet Maria but plans to shoot her. Corder sneers...

I now await my victim. Will she come? Yes, for women are foolish enough to do anything for the men they errrr!

Behave like a Victorian

If a time machine dropped your dad in Victorian London would he act like a gentleman . . . or a slob? Test him with these 'do' and 'don't' problems taken from a book of Gentlemen's Manners and see if he could have been accepted by polite Victorians. Just one problem . . . if he makes a single mistake he could well be frowned on for the rest of his life!

Do or don't...

48. offer your hand to an older person to be shaken.
49. eat from the side of your soup spoon and not the end.
50. write to people you know on post cards.
51. remove your overcoat before you enter someone's living room.
52. use slang words.
53. bite into your bread at dinner.
54. call your servants 'girls'.
55. raise your hat to a lady in the street.
56. spit on the pavement.
57. sit with legs crossed.

Manchester misery

58. Not many men in Victorian England were gentlemen – which was unfortunate because gentlemen lived longer than working men. If you were an upper class person living in Manchester in 1842 you could expect to live 38 years (on average). But, if you were in the working class what was the average you could expect to live?

a) 37 years
b) 27 years
c) 17 years

LIFE'S NOT SO BAD SON...IF THEY DON'T WORK YER TOO MUCH, AND A MACHINE DON'T KILL YER, AND YER DON'T STARVE, AND YER DON'T GET POISONED, OR FROZEN, OR DISEASED, OR SACKED, OR CRIPPLED OR IN DEBT, OR PUT IN PRISON, OR ......

Trasseno talk

'Trasseno' was a name for Victorian villains. They had their own way of life in the slums, and they also had their own language. What would you say to a Trasseno if he (or she) said these things to you? Would you answer 'Yes' or 'No'? Be careful! Give the wrong answer to some and something very nasty could happen...

59. 'Do you fancy a chat?'
60. 'Would you like me to nail your broken door?'
61. 'Shall I give you this finny?'
62. 'Do you think teachers should give their pupils dewskitches?'
63. 'Want a ride on my flummut horse?'
64. 'Would you like to put a jack under the wheel of my carriage?'

65. 'Are you flat?'
66. 'Is your father a nammo?'
67. 'Shall I invite some jolly people to your party?'
68. 'Do you wear a flag when you are cooking?'

Odd one out

The Victorians were great inventors. There are fifteen inventions in this picture . . . but only ten were first produced between 1800 and 1900, anywhere in the world. Can you spot the odd ones out and the odd ones in?

Name that kid

Parents sometimes gave their children curious names, and the Victorians were no different. Which of the following are real Victorian first names and which are not?

84. YETTY

85. BRAINED

86. QUINCE

87. POMEGRANATE

88. DESPAIR

89. GAZZA

90. MURDER

91. VENUS

92. FEATHER

93. STARKEY

Howzat Victoria?

The English lost a cricket match against Australia for the first time in 1880. They burned a bail to ashes and have played for those Ashes ever since. 'How's that?' cricketers cry (or 'Howzat?' in cricket language) when they think a batsman is out. And 'Howzat?' is the question about these curious Queen Victoria facts.

94. She was the shortest *and* the longest reigning monarch Britain ever had! Howzat?

95. Victoria was responsible for the death of her beloved husband, Albert. Howzat?

96. The police set Victoria up as the target for a murdering gunman. Howzat?

97. Victoria was highly respectable all her life yet she caused a scandal in her coffin. Howzat?

98. Albert and Victoria were married in 1840 though he never proposed to her. Howzat?

99. The Victorians liked portrait paintings but she preferred a particular kind. Howzat?

100. Victoria was Queen of England yet the 'Queen's English' was never very good. Howzat?

Christmas Dickens

Believe it or not, by the early part of the 1800s Christmas had almost died out. People thought it was a silly, old-fashioned custom and didn't want to be bothered with it any more.

Charles Dickens, with his story *A Christmas Carol*, did more than anyone to change all that. The tale of Scrooge, the Cratchits and Tiny Tim has been a smash hit from Victorian times to the present day.

Here's a quick Victorian Christmas quiz for anyone who thinks they know about books...

101. How long did it take Charles Dickens to write *A Christmas Carol*?
a) 22 years
b) 2 years
c) 2 months

102. How long did it take for the book to be a hit?
a) It was slow at first but sold out in 10 years.
b) It was an instant success and sold out as soon as it appeared.
c) By the following Christmas (1844) it had sold out.

103. What did Dickens say about his book?
a) 'I was a bit surprised because I've written much better.'
b) 'I'm amazed no one else had the idea. I pinched it from an old Scottish story.'
c) 'The greatest I think I have ever achieved.'

104. Dickens made still more money from the book by doing what?
a) Travelling around the country reading it to the public.
b) Making a record of the story and selling the record.
c) Turning it into a pantomime and acting the part of Scrooge himself.

105. What effect did Dickens's success have on him?
a) All the travelling and performing killed him.
b) It made a jealous writer kill him.
c) It made him so rich his wife killed him to get her hands on his money.

106. When Dickens died it was a shock to the Christmas industry. One little girl said what?
a) 'Does that mean that Father Christmas is dead?'
b) 'Does that mean Tiny Tim is dead?'
c) 'Does that mean there'll be no more Christmases?'

THIS IS A DICKENS OF A NOVEL

HOW THE DICKENS DID HE DO IT?

WHAT A DICKENS DICKENS'S DICKENS IS!

American Civil War quiz

During Queen Victoria's reign, a civil war was raging on the other side of the Atlantic Ocean. How much do you know about it? Torment your teacher or pester your parent with these fiendishly fascinating but fairly foul questions:

107. Rebel General Robert E Lee died on 12 October 1870 at Lexington, Virginia. He should have been buried in full uniform but they left his boots off. Why?
a) Because his feet had swelled and they couldn't get them back on the corpse.
b) Because the coffin was too small. It was a choice of leaving the boots off or slicing a bit off the top of his head.

c) Because his starving wife had cooked his boots to make a stew for the funeral guests.

108. Rebel General Beauregard was famous for this thick black hair. It turned grey during the war. Why?
a) Because he ran out of hair dye.
b) Because the horrors of war turned his hair grey with shock.
c) Because he dyed it grey to escape capture.

109. Yank General McClellan was defeated by 'Quaker Guns'. What was so unusual about them?
a) They fired backwards so when you thought you were safe they shot you.
b) They made so much noise they made you quake till the buttons fell off your tunic and your trousers fell down.

c) They couldn't fire at all because they were made of wood.

110. Rebel General Thomas J Jackson, nicknamed 'Stonewall' Jackson, did something strange with his right forefinger. What?
a) He stood with it pointing up at the sky.
b) He lost it in a goat's mouth when he went to stroke the creature.
c) He bit his nails so hard he chewed the finger off.

111. The Rebels were short of gunpowder because it was all made in Yankee America. They found a way to make it using what?
a) Buffalo poo.
b) Frog guts.
c) Human piddle.

112. Two Rebel brothers, Jasper and Jack Walker, each lost one in the Civil War. What?
a) A leg.
b) A mother.
c) A bet.

113. Jefferson Davis was the first and last President of the Rebel Americans. What bright idea did he bring to the Reb armies?

a) Reindeer to pull them through the snowy mountains.

b) Dolphins to pull their ships into battle when it was calm.

c) Camels to help them fight in the desert.

HMM...PART OF THIS PLAN IS NOT RIGHT

114. Yankee Benjamin Franklin Butler was given command of New Orleans and was hated by the defeated Rebels. They got their own back by putting his picture on what?

a) The front of dartboards for piercing.

b) The bottom of pots for piddling.

c) The middle of handkerchiefs for polluting.

WHO'S BEEN THROWING DARTS AT MY PIDDLING POT?

115. Rebel General Forrest hated black people. What was he said to do to black Yankee soldiers he captured?

a) Starve them to death.

b) Bury them alive.

c) Use them as slaves to serve his dinner.

116. Yankee troops captured Rebel General Robert E Lee's tobacco plantation. They took out the tobacco and planted what?

a) Corpses.

b) General Lee's treasure so they could come back and find it after the war.

c) Explosive mines to kill the General if he ever returned.

Answers

The gorgeous Georgians

Quick questions

1. She was locked away back in Germany. This was her punishment for flirting with Count Konigsmark. It was worse for the count. He'd been murdered and secretly buried at the castle. Jolly George.

2. He collected the skins of the dogs. He was probably happy to do this because one of his other jobs was to sweep up doggy poo from the streets!

3. He had both hands chopped off.

4. It's said Blackbeard's headless corpse swam round the ship three times before finally sinking!

5. They believed it helped their eyesight.

6. He cut it open to see how an elephant's body works.

7. Because she had been hanged once and pronounced dead. As she was taken off to the graveyard in her coffin she sat up! Lucky Maggie lived another 30 years before dying a second time – for good.

8. George died on his way to the funeral. He had held up Dorothea's funeral for six months. If he'd been quicker he'd have had the pleasure of seeing her put six feet under.

9. George had said that he would visit her after his death. She believed the raven was George. Caw! Imagine that!

10. Turpin's school master betrayed him.

11. Burning a hole through the lobe of your ear was supposed to cure the pain in the tooth. Crazy! If you ever see your dentist with a hot poker you know it's time to change dentists.

12. The public could buy tickets to watch George II and the royal family dine. You could try selling tickets for your neighbours to watch you eat your beans on toast!

13. Grab the head of the goose and tear it off. This was made harder by greasing the goose's beak.

14. As soon as it heard enemy gunfire it ran away. George couldn't stop it! The fat little feller had to go back to his command on foot.

15. He was hanged. The bagpipes were declared 'an instrument of war' after the Scottish Jacobite rebellion of 1745. Happily it is now legal to play these beautiful melodic instruments.

16. Spectators crowded on to wooden stands to watch Lovat get lopped. The stands collapsed and killed 20 people. Served them right.

17. It killed him. In 1751 he caught a chill but it was the stomach damage, caused by the ball, that finished him off.

18. They cut off his nose. They then dumped him down a well but two days later he was still alive. They threw logs down the well to finish him off. After that he didn't feel too well.

19. He had committed suicide. A suicide's spirit was supposed to haunt the earth. By burying him at a cross-roads he wouldn't know which way to turn so he'd have to stay there. The stake through the heart helped.

20. They believed that raw fruits caused the plague.

21. He ate the whole chicken – guts, feathers and all – and it was alive. At least it was when he started eating.

22. Banknote forgery. Richard Vaughan had the honour of being the first man to be hanged for copying the notes. Now you know why your teachers tell you not to copy!

23. They thought her upturned nose made her look just like a pug dog. The German queen didn't understand and thought they were shouting 'God save the Queen'!

24. Mouse skin was used to make false eyebrows.

25. The sheep struggled and pulled the rope tight around the thief's neck. He was strangled –

the sheep lived, you'll be pleased to hear. A lesson for all ram-raiders.

26. Boomerangs. The country is Australia.

27. They dumped the tea into the harbour. Many rebels at the 'Boston Tea Party' were disguised as Native American Indians. It was part of a revolution which was to see the Brits thrown out.

28. The cow choked on a pin and died. And the hills were alive with the sound of moo-sick.

29. Brodie was the first man to be executed on the machine. He was a councillor by day but a burglar by night.

30. Elizabeth was just two years old when she died. At least skinny Lizzie would have fitted in her pram.

31. He was wearing a beard. Silly, but true.

32. Top hats.

33. George III was sure poor George III was dead. His mental illness was sad. The treatments his doctors gave him were really mad. One was to shout at the king while his mouth was stuffed with handkerchiefs so he couldn't shout back.

34. Gunpowder. Boom! Boom!

35. They use them to make false teeth for human patients.

36. Four years old. The sweeps weren't supposed to be under nine but employers lied about the ages of their workers.

37. Pickled in a barrel of brandy. It preserved the body – and the sailors drank the brandy afterwards!

38. He shot the Prime Minister, Spencer Perceval, dead. The only Brit PM to be assassinated. Bellingham was hanged.

39. His arm. He also almost lost his wedding ring when the arm was amputated. 'Here! Bring that arm back!' he cried from his hospital bed.

40. The 'treadmill' – a bit like a hamster wheel, where the prisoners walk and walk and go nowhere.

41. *Frankenstein*. Monstrous Mary was only 18 when she dreamed up this story of a man put together like a Lego kit. Seriously weird writer.

42. Wilson was sentenced to be hanged, drawn and quartered. In fact he was hanged then beheaded. His 'crime' was to lead a march in protest against unemployment.

43. A pumpkin. She probably changed it each time she rode, which is more than she did with her stockings. She wore them till they stank.

44. Tights. He had them made the colour of his flesh because he didn't want to look like a wimp.

45. Rugby. He picked up the ball and ran with it. The game was named after his public school, Rugby, so we don't say, 'Fancy a game of Ellis?'

46. Huskisson stepped from his carriage to say hello to friends, was hit by a train and died.

47. The disease of cholera. Not only does it give you disgusting diarrhoea but victims turn blue before they die. 20,000 died in the next year.

Dreadful down under

48. c) They thought they looked like bad news, and they were right!

49. c)

50. c)

51. c) John Hudson was a nine-year-old chimney sweep.

Foul for females

52. True.

53. False. The average age was about 24. Very few married under 16.

54. True. But this law was changed in 1789 and the punishment was changed to hanging.

55. True. It wasn't legal but it sometimes happened – and continued to happen until 1887.

56. True. But the stick he used had to be no thicker than his thumb, so that's all right.

57. False. But they did use lead paint, arsenic powder and plaster of Paris.

58. False. They would be paid about £3 a year.

59. True.

60. True. In 1797 a small group of women from Pembrokeshire, led by Jemima Nicholas, captured 20 men from the invading French. They were so terrifying that the French army surrendered.

61. False. A pale skin was beautiful to the Georgians and women would sometimes wear a mask in front of the face to protect the skin.

Out of time

62. Steam engine – No. The first recorded one was in 1698. The 1700s did see the first steam powered vehicle though.

63. Piano – Yes. First in Britain in 1711, brought from Rome.

64. Bathroom with hot and cold running water – Yes. In 1701 at Chatsworth, Derbyshire.

65. Police detective – No. First appeared in France in 1812. Though there were policemen called Bow Street Runners by 1749 in London.

66. Roller skates – Yes. Worn by Joseph Merlin to a musical party in 1760. He skated into the ballroom, playing a violin. Sadly he lost control, skated into a £500 mirror, smashed it, smashed his violin and almost cut himself to shreds.

67. Jigsaw puzzle – Yes. First seen in 1763. The oldest surviving one is a 1767 map of England where you have to fit the counties in the right place. Very educational.

68. Sewing machine – Yes. First seen in London in 1790. Designed to sew leather boots and shoes.

69. Post Office letter box – No. First seen in Britain in 1809, but the first red pillar box didn't appear until 1852. Before the first letter box a man walked round the streets ringing a bell.

70. Railway bridge – Yes. Causey Arch, County Durham was built in 1727 ... even though steam trains weren't invented! The wooden railway carried horse-drawn coal trucks.

71. Iron boat – Yes. John Wilkinson built a 20-metre barge in 1787, not the first iron ship but by far the biggest.

72. Tinned food – No. Introduced to Britain in 1812. The French came up with the idea in 1795 but used glass bottles.

Test your teacher

73.b) A 'pelican' was a tool for pulling out difficult teeth. The instrument got its name because it looked like a pelican's beak.

74.a) The dog died. Smuggled tea wasn't always as pure as the stuff you get in your tea bags.

75.a) Robinson Cruso, a bed-maker, lived in King's Lynn High Street. The writer Daniel Defoe visited King's Lynn on his travels and must have seen the name Robinson Cruso outside the shop, because he called his famous book *Robinson Crusoe*.

76.b) The highwayman couldn't afford a pistol. The guard wasn't fooled and shot the robber dead.

77.c) Peasants wore trousers to work in the fields and a gentleman would not be so common as to wear them. Gentlemen wore tighter fitting 'breeches' with stockings.

78.a) And the biscuits were often worse than the cheese – full of black-headed maggots.

79.b) When it was used in a mine it could explode 'fire damp' gas. It killed a lot of miners. Spedding went speeding to his death when he tested it.

80.c)

81.c) A 'stink-trap' is a bend in the toilet pipe that stops smells coming up from the drains.

Very useful. Your toilet has this useful bend, so don't try to straighten it.

82.c) That's right. Hare 'coursing' as it's called is still enjoyed today by many people and many packs of hounds. That's life, hare today, gone tomorrow.

Foreign affairs

83. Head. After taking their revenge, the Samurai warriors killed themselves so they could join their lord in death.

84. Slave. Tens of thousands of Africans were snatched from their villages and transported to be slaves in America.

85. Ear. Jenkins refused to pay Spanish customs tax. The Spanish sliced off his ear and told him to take it back to his king. He did! The fighting that followed became known as 'The War of Jenkins's Ear'. (Just as well they didn't cut a slice off his bum!)

86. Skeleton. King Charles III ordered workers to dig under the volcanic ash of Vesuvius. They found the well preserved ruins of Pompeii where bodies were 'frozen' as they died in AD 79.

87. Tongue. Peter died in a scuffle and his body-guard said he couldn't remember what happened. This is a very useful story if you ever find yourself in trouble!

88. Naked woman. The paintings were very popular but mostly with men for some reason.

89. Witch. The Emperor also banned tortures such as the rack but he kept flogging and branding. Kind man.

90. Leg. The unfortunate British soldier was about to have his leg amputated when a stray cannonball blew off the other and killed him before he could hop off the operating table.

91. Boat. A Hawaiian chief 'borrowed' Captain Cook's boat so Cook led an attack of sailors with guns against Hawaiians with spears. The Hawaiians weren't afraid of the guns because they'd never seen them before. Cook was killed.

92. Frog. Galvani was working with 'static' electricity and noticed the effect of the charge on a dead frog, they say. But what was a dead frog doing in his lab?

93. Copper bottom. It stopped the weeds and barnacles clinging to the hull and slowing the ship down. (Please note: 'Copper bottom' is not the answer to no. 87!)

94. Corpse. The French tested the guillotine on dead bodies from a local hospital before using it on a live criminal. When the French Revolution started in 1793 the guillotine was used on tens of thousands, faster than a chip-shop chipper.

A revolutionary question

95. In the chopping centre

Chop and change

96-106. ALL are true. That's a lot of ouis.

Wacky words

107.g) 108.e) 109.a) 110.h) 111.c) 112.j) 113.b) 114.i) 115.d) 116.f)

The vile Victorians

Quick questions

1. She was 18.

2. Women (and boys under 10) were no longer allowed to work in mines. They lost their wages so it isn't all good news.

3. Glasgow.

4. It was a sign of bad weather on the way. People were glad of the warning. Modern weather forecasts smell better.

5. The potato crop failed.

6. In Ireland. It marked the end of the Young Rebellion.

7. 'The train's so slow, I was 12 when I got on it.' On most lines 30 mph was thought to be quite fast enough.

8. They were looking for coins and metal dropped through drains. Would you stick your hand down a toilet for your pocket money? Toshers would.

9. They were emigrating from Ireland because they were starving in the potato famine. The old ships, nicknamed coffin ships, didn't always make it. Starve or drown? Some choice.

10. It rained heavily and many people stayed at home rather than get wet.

11. It was made of glass.

12. It was the first flushing public toilet for men – but not women, who would have to keep their legs crossed!

13. Convicts. Australia was a dumping ground for Brit criminals and now it stopped. Brit criminals got harsher sentences at home instead and no kangaroo steaks.

14. They were dumped outside the hospital and eaten by pigs. Then the pigs were eaten by the patients ... including the patients who lost arms and legs. You could say they ended up eating themselves! Yeuch!

15. It snapped.

16. Soccer. The new rules said that only the goalkeeper could handle the ball. It also banned fighting on the pitch. Someone should tell today's players!

17. Canada! Yes it sounds odd but with the help of US troops the Irish rebels attacked Brit troops in Canada as the first stage of attacking Brit troops in Ireland.

18. It was the first detective novel.

19. Moustaches. Sailors could be clean shaven or wear beards, but moustaches were popular with soldiers and the navy didn't want its men to look like their great rivals in the army!

20. Charles Dickens. He was only 58 but was racing around the country, reading and acting his characters. It killed him.

21. Go to school. The Education Reform Act forced everyone to suffer at school whether they liked it or not.

22. 'Yes.' Not very chatty when someone had come all that way to interview him, was it?

23. She was made Empress of India.

24. None. The inspector wasn't trained and had never inspected a bridge before. He wouldn't have known a bad bridge if it had jumped up and bitten him on the nose.

25. The first Christmas tree lights.

26. George Eliot was a woman, real name Mary Anne Evans. She didn't think publishers would print a book by a woman so she lied and said she was a man.

27. The ship slid into the river, rolled over and drowned 124 of them. Well, they built it, so they couldn't complain – and they didn't.

28. A Bible. Very cool. Unfortunately the Bible was no defence against the spear that killed him.

29. Jack the Ripper. He killed eight women and the mystery has never been forgotten – or solved.

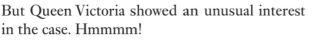

But Queen Victoria showed an unusual interest in the case. Hmmmm!

30. An elephant. Joseph Merrick was known as the Elephant Man and he was treated as a freak, rather than a sick person. He died aged just 27.

31. The Sioux Indians.

32. Smaller. Blackpool Tower is only half the height of the Eiffel Tower – but people falling off the top end up with exactly the same amount of deadness.

33. The kangaroos were in the first cinema show in Britain. Now you know the answer you'll be hoppy.

34. Motorists were now allowed to drive without being led by a man with a red flag. The speed limit also went up from 4 mph to 20 mph. Scary!

35. It was a savings club. People would save money, and at Christmas they'd have enough to buy a goose!

36. An early hang glider.

37. Glass eyes. His favourite was a bloodshot eye which he used when he had a cold!

38. Tins of chocolate.

39. They kissed the corpse's hand.

40. Red was supposed to be a royal colour.

A royal question

41. They both have 'the' as their middle name! Boring answer: William the Fourth was a sailor, and so was Popeye.

Umms and errs

42. Mother. 'On the telephone' is definitely wrong! So is 'a taxi'.

43. Die. 'Fight and win' would not be very English – look at the present-day cricket team.

44. Pity. 'Bury' makes a bit more sense, you have to admit.

45. Unhand. Not a word you'll hear very often but remember it next time [...] grabs you!

46. Polish. This is such a famous [...] granny probably knows it. In fact she probably ate the pies!

47. Love. 'Get chocolates from' is not a good enough answer.

Behave like a Victorian

48. Don't. Wait until they have offered it to you.

49. Do. And remember you mustn't gurgle or suck in your breath while you sip your soup.

50. Don't. Write letters or nothing at all.

51. Do. Even if it's only a very short call.

52. Don't. Well, usually. There are some slang words that a gentleman may use. If you don't know what they are then avoid slang altogether.

53. Don't. Break off a piece and place it in your mouth.

54. Don't. Call them maids or servants.

55. Do. BUT ... wait till she has bowed to you first and do not wave your hat in the air the way the French do – put it straight back on to your head.

56. Don't. Or anywhere else for that matter!

57. Don't. The book admits that most men do this but says it is extremely impolite.

Manchester misery

58. c) In London slums people would, on average, live 22 years – but average upper class people would live twice as long. The unhealthiest place to live in 1842 was Liverpool, where the average age of death was just 15 years old. Queen Victoria lived to be 81. The average age was so low because lots of children died very young.

Trasseno talk

59. No. A 'chat' was a louse that crawls around your body. Are you sure you fancy one?

60. No. To 'nail' something is to 'steal' it. Doors were popular for sleeping on. Propped up on a few bricks, a door would keep you off the damp floor – unfortunately it wasn't high enough to keep the rats off you.

61. Yes. Well, maybe. . . A 'finny' was a five pound note, but be careful because a Trasseno might try to give you some 'flash' money – a worthless imitation. The forgers didn't try to copy money – that was a serious offence and you could be hanged for it until 1832. Instead they made notes that looked like money, but with the 'Bank of Engraving' written on them instead of the 'Bank of England'.

62. No. A 'dewskitch' was a beating – usually with a strap, a birch (a bundle of twigs) or a cane.

63. No. 'Flummut' meant dangerous.

64. No. A 'jack' was Trasseno language for a policeman. Of course policemen were also called 'Bobbies' or 'Peelers' because they were organized by Sir Robert Peel.

65. No. A 'flat' person wasn't someone who's been squashed by a flummut horse! It was someone who is easily tricked ... and you wouldn't admit that!

66. No. 'Nammo' should really be spelled 'namow' because it meant 'woman' (spelled backwards). Most back-slang words have slipped out of use – we no longer say 'yennap' for a penny and no one drinks 'reeb' any more. But you might still be a 'yob'!

67. No. A 'jolly' person was one who starts a fight in public! They could be useful; they'd start a fight and get everyone's attention so that the fine-wirers, flimps and gonophs (pick-pockets) could go to work stealing unguarded purses.

68. Yes. Well, you should... 'Flag' means apron.

Odd one out

69. Hot air balloon – OUT. First flight made in 1783 near Paris.

70. Aeroplane – OUT. Orville Wright made the first powered heavier-than air flight in 1903.

71. Parachute – OUT because the first jump was made from a hot-air balloon in 1797. You can be excused for getting this one wrong because the first jump in Britain was in 1802 and the first jump by a British person (who lived) was in 1838. The year before a Brit died trying.

72. Multi-storey car park – OUT . . . but only just. In May 1901 an electric carriage company built a 7-storey garage for its vehicles.

73. Telephone – IN-vented 1876. US inventor Alexander Graham Bell usually gets the credit for this. (Although Johann Reis of Germany did show a telephone device in 1860 made of a violin case and a sausage skin!)

74. Box kite – IN-vented in Australia, 1893.

75. Photographic camera – IN-vented in the 1820s and 30s.

76. Railway signal box – IN-vented in London 1839.

77. Railway station – IN-vented in Baltimore, USA, in 1830.

78. Policeman – OUT. The London police force was created in 1829 but the world's first was in Paris 1667.

79. Motor car – IN-vented in France in 1862. The 19th century also saw the first road death (London 1896), drunken driver (London 1897), car theft (Paris 1896) and speeding motorist (Kent 1896).

80. Railway locomotive – IN-vented in 1804 by Richard Trevithick. The Victorian age was the age of the railways with steam trains crossing the country. The first railway death was in 1828, when driver John Gillespie's boiler blew up on the famous Stockton and Darlington railway.

81. Pedal cycle – IN-vented in Scotland in 1839.

82. Football goal nets. IN-vented by a Liverpool engineer in 1890.

83. Women footballers – IN-vented in 1895 by Lady Florence Dixie who formed the British Women's Football Club.

Name that kid
84–93. All are true – except 87 and 89.

Howzat Victoria?
94. She was the shortest in height but the longest in the time she spent on the throne.

95. The dirty water from her toilet leaked into Albert's drinking water and gave him the disease that killed him.

96. The gunman tried to shoot her as she drove in her carriage in London. His gun misfired and he escaped. The police told her to drive in the same place and at the same time the next day so that he could try again. He did! They caught him.

97. She was buried with a photograph of her 'friend', her Scottish servant. In her hand was a lock of his hair. What had they been up to when she was alive, people wanted to know!

98. Victoria proposed to him!

99. Victoria (and hubby Albert) preferred the people in the pictures to have no clothes on!

100. She was from the German Hanover family so she always spoke with a German accent.

Christmas Dickens
101.c) He was a very fast writer.

102.b) The book was published on 17 December 1843 and immediately sold out.

103.c) Well, if you can't praise your own work, who can?

104.a) *A Christmas Carol* was so popular that Dickens was asked to read from it in public.

His reading from this book (and bits of his longer novels) drew large audiences in England and America, and Dickens made as much money from them as he did from his writing.

105.a) It was said he 'died of fame'.

106.a) Although Charles Dickens had not even mentioned Father Christmas in his story, the little girl's remark shows how important to Christmas the famous author had become.

American Civil War quiz
107.b) A flood had washed away all the undertaker's coffins. Eventually one coffin was rescued downriver from the flood. It was too short for Lee's six-foot corpse, so he was buried without his boots..

108.a) Vain Beauregard didn't want to show his age so he dyed his hair with Yankee dye. But when the war came he couldn't get the dye from the enemy and his hair turned back to its true grey colour.

109.c) The Rebels often used this trick – and it always worked! It's a bit like a robber holding up a bank with a sawn-off cucumber!

110.a)

111.c) George ordered his men to dig up old toilets and make saltpetre for the gunpowder from the stale pee!

112.a)

113.c)

114.b) Butler was balding, fat and cross-eyed. Imagine that face staring up at you when you sat on a toilet pot!

115.b) This was the story, though Forrest always said it was a lie.

116.a) They buried their Rebel enemies there. It's now Arlington National Cemetery.